*Jasmine Nights & Monkey Pluck: Love, Discovery and Tea*

December, 2002

To Shogo Sato,

Thank you for the
gift of the tea ceremony.

Kathleen
Willett

# Jasmine Nights & Monkey Pluck: Love, Discovery and Tea

Writings Collected by Marylu Downing, Faith Morgan & Ellen Galford

PHOTOGRAPHS BY ELLEN GALFORD AND FAITH MORGAN

Printed in Singapore
First Printing

Jasmine Nights & Monkey Pluck:
Love, Discovery and Tea
*Collected and edited by*
Marylu Downing, Ellen Galford and
Faith Morgan – 1st ed.

Preassigned LCCN: 2001098396
ISBN 0-9649497-4-1
1. American Literature – Women authors
2. Tea  3. Inspiration
4. Women authors, literary
collections  5. Poetry

Cover and book design and layout:
Bob Bingenheimer
Photo Scans: John Morgan
Photo of Teacups Group: Aubri Lane
All teacup photos by Faith Morgan
and Ellen Galford

Fionna Perkins' *First Date* was also
published in the *Redwood Coast Review*
and in *The Horse Orchard*, (Forestville:
Floreant Press, 2000).

Terry Ehret's *World in Need of Braiding*,
originally appeared in *Translations from
the Human Language* (San Francisco:
Sixteen Rivers Press, 2001).

Carmen Castillo's *Jonathon* appeared
in *The Dickens*.

Published by Floreant Press/Teacups Group

Floreant Press
Teacups Group
12655 Fiori Lane
Sebastopol, CA 95472

# Contents

# Introduction

Long time friends connecting during a busy week, we sliced hot persimmon bread to eat with our tea. As we laughed and talked and sipped from our teacups, we got the idea for this book. We wanted to create a beautiful book that would convey a sense of the human spirit, a book to catch glimpses of what women discuss with each other over a cup of tea.

For inspiration we sent pictures of teacups to writers and poets and invited them to create work containing a sense of abundance, pieces that celebrate the ironies and simple pleasures of daily life. We were surprised and pleased with what came back: delicious sensual fantasies, leaving home at 17, the difficult birth of a child, a harried visit with a fussy friend, tea divinities and root cellars. Writers sent stories and poems focused on moments that change our thinking – epiphanies that sprinkle lightly down upon us, and others that almost bowl us over.

We have met together often to read and edit, to take photographs, and to borrow teacups and pots from friends and antique stores. Always, we stopped for our tea break, sometimes at a local bakery where we shared a pastry or two.

We hope you will take time for yourself – a reading break for a story or poem and a cup of tea.

*Marylu Downing, Ellen Galford and Faith Morgan*
*Sebastopol, California, July, 2002*

## Invitation to Tea

There are men I have fantasized seducing in roadhouses with beer and barbecued oysters. I picture us laughing and leaning toward each other over a chipped Formica tabletop, the jukebox roaring, our kisses a cool stew of bitters and brine. Others have popped up in dreams of deserted beaches, mountaintops, empty theaters, offices, Venetian gondolas, used-car lots.

But you I have imagined arriving for tea. You sit across from me in a fire-warmed parlor, nervous and elegant in proper winter wool. Next to you on the stiffly upholstered couch is a bunch of Parma violets and the volume of Keats you are returning. I have just poured dark and smoky Lapsang Souchong into cups of oriental porcelain, adding without asking a few grains of sugar, small clouds of milk. You accept your cup with an air of slight surprise, but as your eyes meet mine over the lustered rim, I see that I have gotten it right. Outside, the rain starts. Now your gaze takes in the plates of brandied pear slices, shortbread spiced with cardamom and ginger, the ticking clock, the sleeping tiger cat. Life has become a poem. It begins with "Yes."

*Susan Bono*

# Beginning

At the ebb of night
the new moon reveals
a seam
at the edge of fabricated fullness.
Dawn approaching
empties shadow into light
bringing green to the shaded leaf.

The owl calls three times
from the cavity of its chest
from the hollow of a tree
across the distance to the house.

In the palm of a hand,
morning.

*Sarah Flowers*

# Bergamot, Bee Balm, Genus Monarda

*In* our Ohio village, bergamot grew thick and aromatic in Emily Powers' backyard flower beds, but being dreamy and boy-crazy, I knew nothing of herbs then, or teas. Emily's oldest son, David, was the boy I was crazy for, and, maybe because Emily was a Quaker, he had gentle, refined ways of showing passion.

Once, after dark, he appeared under the pink dogwood that grew to the height of my second story bedroom window. He climbed up as far as the branches would hold him and began singing *Sanctus* in a plaintive tenor voice.

My girlhood bedroom had pink wallpaper with a shepherd-shepherdess theme. I took calls on a pink princess phone. This night, seated on the hope chest my mother had stocked with embroidered percale pillowcases and dainty demitasse cups, I peered down at David, loving him behind a pane of glass.

When David left I ran down to see what flower he had left on the back step this time. (I saved each one, pressing them between book pages, salting them with cloves and cinnamon.) It was a tufted scarlet bergamot, and I pressed it, stem and all, never to forget its name or scent.

When we buried my father in Ohio this spring, I slept in my old room. I found the apothecary jar full of pungent potpourri, the bergamot perfectly intact. Graveside, I looked up and met David's gaze as our son dropped ashes into a small square hole.

*Sanctus.*

*Jane Holly Love*

# Tea Divinity

Whenever my grandfather drank o-cha, the tea gods came out of hiding. He inhaled his boiling tea, filling the entire kitchen with his melodic slurping – which somehow crescendoed – then he swallowed, and breathed out "aaahhhh," deep from his throat, mouth fully open. Tea smoke billowed from his mouth and nostrils, as the steam from his cup curled toward the heavens. He gazed out, glassy-eyed, as the tea gods paraded in front of him.

But I could only imagine all their singing, their dancing, their reveling, for they never allowed *me* to see them. One night, I tiptoed out of my room, curled up like a cat under the kitchen table, with a blanket around me, and waited.

The chirpy sips of my grandmother having her morning o-cha – half oolong, half Sencha – woke me.

"Obaachan," I whispered, "did you see them?"

"The tea gods? Again? Oh, yes. You just *missed* them."

"What? I missed them?" I buried my face in my pillow.

"Nobody can trick the tea gods, dear. Just keep the spirit of tea in your heart, and they'll come. Be patient."

I steeped myself in tea culture for years. Tea leaves, teacups, teapots, tea medicine, teas for different moods. I loved it all. Sometimes I even drank o-cha like Grandpa. One day, though, I found myself silently sipping three times, holding the tea in my mouth, closing my eyes, putting my head back, and then ending with a quiet gulp. And I did it again. And again. "Aaahhhh." Tea divinities swirled around me – in glorious abundance!

*Lori Kuwabara*

# World in Need of Braiding

This time of year our hands reach for the ends of things, twist patterns out of reflected light, out of water, loaves of bread. We lie down on the grass beside those we have disappointed, dry, unforgiven. We are supposed to be eating, preparing to sleep, filling the storerooms with enough color, dividing the universe into light and dark. But the dry grass, the purple thistles, the burrs in our socks want our attention. They are old. They are dying. They need us to listen to their stories, the same as last year.

"Not much breath left," say the grasses, and the brittle gates of the hill swing open. We love this season of loose connections, excess of prepositions, the long shadows of the corn. And now the carriage of darkness rides into view, bright yellow wheels and spokes like unfriendly laughter. Now the long carriage of night gathering speed.

Take us slowly down the wind-sea, this plenitude of death. Slowly, slowly run the last of the daylight, riding  away the sun. We come wobbling, void of course, shaking in our inadequate clothes. We need time to lie down in the evening shadows we love, to stretch our heart beyond its cage of silence, to pull what grows, richly and abundantly, towards us.

*Terry Ehret*

# Blackberries

At the first house, blackberries are a novelty. I carefully wind thin shoots through the fence, my baby watching from her playpen. The hardy vines soon spill onto the street. "Get rid of them now, before they take over," warns a neighbor. But that summer we lovingly feed each other berries hot off the vine, warm berry juices bursting inside our mouths. I learn to prune thorny suckers wearing gloves and a long-sleeved shirt.

At the second house we don't pay attention. Blackberries, always reaching for new terrain, spring up everywhere. I imagine us trapped inside a prickly nest like the feral kittens my daughter, wearing long prom gloves, carefully lifts from their thorny home. I pluck blackberries every morning. Abundant, sweet, and free for cereal, shortcakes, jam, or just in a bowl with a cup of tea. "The price you have to pay," we say to each other rubbing our stinging scratches with ice. We hire a man to contain the blackberries. He digs them out by their roots.

At the third house I carefully search for vines before we buy the property; it seems we have no berries. I'm relieved to be rid of sticky messes and the intrusive growth of insistent suckers. "What will we do for pies?" my daughter asks, holding our grandson. A few weeks later I see small ragged leaves. Blackberries! Cut back to the ground for the house sale, they push up from a vast root system. I pull out all the vines I find, except for one by the back fence. I will grow just this one patch... for the mornings, for the sweet hot juices.

*Marylu Downing*

## Marble Mountains

My first train ride from Pisa to Pietrasanta feels like coming home: dry hot hills, red clay tile roofs, white and peach stucco walls, marble mountains. The street below my third floor window is an echo chamber, magnifying children at play, people meeting, greeting, laughing in the nearby Piazza Duomo. Late into the heat of a summer's night, I wait for you, hanging out my window, drinking it all in as the sky fades from blue to red to peach over the rooftops, and late diners stroll arm-in-arm by lighted shop windows. "I am sure to see you first," I think, but no, your quiet knock sounds. Breathing quickens, as, with spirals of sensation, desire, l leave the window for the unknown.

Both of us sculptors of cold hard stone, our first touch is all heat. "I thought you'd never come." But he, like me, couldn't stay away, our beings attuned to one another from the first meeting, longing for this. Eyelids half closed, skin tingling, I laugh and cry for the joy and bone deep touching of this stolen moment. The pure fluid art of our bodies entwined, dancing this age-old dance, with the beauty and grace of soft marble in every move.

In the wee hours of the morning, I walk him through the now quiet streets to his car, arm brushing breast, soft voices, gentle touch. I wish him *buona notte* until next time. Laughing, pleased that I speak his language, we part with a kiss. Knowing it may be the last, our souls are still filled and overflowing.

*Faith Morgan*

# Sacrament

To arrive in Ireland means coming to a place that understands all the implications of tea. We landed in Dublin well after noon on a soft summer's day. Exhilarated and exhausted, we dragged our suitcases up the steps to our board and breakfast in Temple Bar.

"I'll show you to your room," said a red-haired young woman behind the desk.

"But wouldn't you like a cup of tea first?" asked a brunette, peering from the kitchen.

Were they psychic, I wondered, Celtic angels? Of course, we wanted tea first. And so it arrived as we sat in the parlor: two flower sprinkled cups and two flower sprinkled saucers, two spoons, a pot of sugar, a mug of milk, and one large flower sprinkled teapot on a doily covered tray. We hadn't had to explain that though delighted to be here, we were tired, or that though we fully expected to be up and about in no time, we were at the moment disoriented.

The brunette angel stood watching. I poured a cup for myself and one for my companion and set about adding to the deep amber brew. "Perfect," I said, taking a sip. For the numinous Irish, tea is a sacrament – communion with milk and sugar on the side. The angel smiled and slipped away.

Tea implies a moment to oneself, a time to cast your gaze inward while still being present in the world, a time to  give thanks. Some ancient longing had drawn me to this land my mother's family left over a century ago, and, holding my teacup, I felt as welcomed as someone returning home.

*Robin Beeman*

# MacKenzie

My daughter, Fawn, sits, her midsection rising up like an inverted teacup.
She is eight months pregnant; her cup is almost full.

Her older brother, Rich, kneels beside her, his hand on her belly,
a look of delighted amazement on his face. He is feeling the baby move.

His sister is full of new life and they are feeling it together. They're sharing
something they've never shared before and it's a wondrous thing.

The baby, already called MacKenzie, is more wonderful still. Rich
is already in love with his niece, sight unseen.

For him she does not have to be beautiful or gifted, just being is enough.

*Mary Gaffney*

# Brewing Tea

My son has just given the last of my body back.
    He is not interested in nursing;
    cupping the warmth of my skin with tiny fingers
    while his mouth works the milk out,
    roaming my face with his eyes.

When my son points to an object,
chubby arm stretched out with one finger extended,
asking me to name something for him, looking at it with
the long black eyelashes of his father, I cherish
the way only a woman's body can swell with life.
And I say to him "ball, kitten, flower."

But under my breath, so that only he hears,
I tell him to appreciate the earth, the
thick-skinned brown tree trunks,
the brittle green of the grass,
and the gold dahlia petals in the garden.

These are the secret words that a woman tells her son at twilight
in a garden far from the city while her teakettle whistles.

*Anne Regan*

# Letter from Home

You've been away now for over a week.
  Things are all right here.  In the morning our
  Girl makes the coffee; I feed the animals.
  I miss you, but not as much as I feared.
  Not with the grinding sorrow I felt
  As a child, when my mother went off
  On the train to visit her aunt and left
  Me smeared with tears on the blank
  Platform, holding my father's hand.  This time
  I know you'll be back.  Still it's disturbing.
  It's as if a piece of the landscape
  Were missing – a hill or a stone – some marker
  That places me here on the planet—
  A sign that tells me I'm home. I think
  Of the cypress trees ranked on the driveway
  Dropping their shattering branches into
  The winter wind. We felled them in August.
  For days after we cut them I drove on
  Past our road as if I were a stranger.

  Without the fixed mark of that presence
  I no longer knew where to turn.

*Laura Gildart Sauter*

## Elixir of the Ages

*I* hold this cup in hand
  warming my palms
  Tea
  Elixir of the ages
  A legacy of humans
  sitting around a pot
  holding a warm vessel
  heating the body
  filling the soul
  circles
  cycles
  of those who
  have stopped to soothe
  with Irish black
  with orange pekoe.

  Soaking up the silence
  holding the circle
  in their hands
  in their souls
  like birds that fly
  together in form
  moving toward the warmth
  like fish that swim in schools
  like children who run after the
  same ball.

*Clara Rosemarda*

# A Story from the Pagoda Teapot

The tea leaves are dreaming. They cry out in their sleep, "How many centuries have we waited here in the darkness?"

The Tea-maker responds, "I brought you here just moments ago."

"Impossible," they say. "We remember nothing of where we were before. And it's too dark to see where we are now."

"You grew between earth and sky," says the Tea-maker, "and you baked in the sun. Now you are inside a rust-colored teapot. Its top is shaped like a pagoda. Its spout is curved and has a finger pointing inward at itself. In form, it is quite beautiful and there is no other teapot like it. In substance, it is no different than you or anything else. And soon –"

But the tea leaves miss the Tea-maker's next words, because they begin to argue. Some argue that the form is the most important; and among these, some say the pagoda, some the spout, and others the pointing finger. They draw pictures of the un-remembered shapes and use them as clubs and shields.

Some say the form matters not at all, only the substance. And among these, many sit and cry in frustration because they cannot see how the substance of tiny green leaves can be "no different than" a solid teapot wall.

At last they grow tired of arguing. One by one, they say, "After all, we know nothing," and grow quiet. They call out to the Tea-maker in one voice, "We want to change."

The Tea-maker speaks as if there had been no interruption. "Soon, I will pour water over you and you will be One. Then you will become greater than you were, and you will be poured into a cup to nourish the Beloved."

If you want to approach this teapot now, be warned that to hear even one note of a song of such melting ecstasy as these leaves are singing could shatter your heart beyond repair.

*Laura Bulkin*

# Orange

*T*he color orange won't leave my mind.

One truth is the fruit: Round, firm, juicy
with an irresistible mantle ripe for peeling.
No continents collided and floated in fractal
disarray to create its pimply pulpy crust.
There are only the ripples of its landless shores:
the tideless ocean of orange.
Peel it and the orange opens to a classical world
of circular symmetry. No chambered nautilus,
spiraling into smaller and smaller crescents,
the orange offers each section in equal portions.
Would you like a piece of my orange?

This is easily offered and accepted.
You are never embarrassed to take such a risk.
You know its limits. There is no vanishing point.
There is only the pulp, the juice, the white seeds
(the promise of a tree). The carbon of its being
never loses its orangeness.

Prokofiev fell in love with three
oranges. Odd only in the mystery of the trinity.
A touch of myth. But where is the archetype
grove of oranges? No orange was offered to Eve
in the Garden of Eden, no orange fell on Newton's head.
But Prokofiev made the dancers fly, leap, and disappear
for three oranges.

*Jane K. Stuppin*

# First Date

Rather than finding a name for the small tea bowls
        held in circled thumbs and forefingers,
we kept refilling, I discover trained monkeys
        in *The Thousand Recipe Chinese Cookbook*
scaling the highest peaks in all China to pick
        tea leaves growing closest to the gods,
dried, infused and sipped later as *Cloud Mist*
        or to credit the workers *Monkey Pluck*.

Another instance of how often I start in one
        direction, and end somewhere else, like
buying the cookbook at a kitchen-store
        closing, where I went for pasta bowls and
a new spatula, or being long rooted into
        the North Coast when my dream was
to travel the world, beginning in China.

Instead I agreed to a date with a young sailor
        who claims I was two hours late. I admit to one,
remembering he out-waited me and wasn't supposed to,
        so here we are fifty-four years later still sitting
across a round table from each other as we did
        in a curtained booth upstairs on Grant Avenue.

When the Chinese waiter brought menus, a pot of tea
        and two little bowls, the young man looked as if
about to be crucified or now that I know the look,
        *poisoned* by the first Chinese meal of his life,
owned up to years after. We didn't ask the name
        of the tea, must have been *Eyebrows of Longevity*.

*Fionna Perkins*

# Cruisin' 50

She laughed at me. In my opinion there was very little to find amusing, which made her laugh even more.

It was the year of my fiftieth birthday, and I was spending every waking minute leading up to that inevitable day, brooding and pouting. I knew that this was, not only a monumental occasion, but also a huge disaster, the likes of which had never been seen before.

Her name was Kathy and we met cruising the Columbia River. She thought that just because she was eighty-something she could tell *me* about turning fifty. Not likely! Much to my chagrin she didn't even try. She just enjoyed herself.

In fact, she enjoyed everything: the sunrise, the sunset, the passing scenery, the Canada geese flying overhead, even an afternoon nap. I wasn't so easily taken in. She brought me a cup of tea and ignored my lack of civility.

She was with an old college sweetheart, a funny man with big ears and sad eyes. They had reconnected after over fifty years of separation, and she was enjoying every minute of their time together.

Her laugh was infectious and finally I just couldn't help myself, I started enjoying the sunrise, the sunset, the Canada geese flying overhead and yes, even an occasional afternoon nap.

It got so bad that one evening, with hands wrapped around our nightly cups of tea, while enjoying the sunset, I realized I had turned fifty and hadn't noticed.

*Marilyn B. Kinghorn*

# Over the Hill

People might think I'm over the hill and I probably am. So, ok, I'm over the hill. Hello to old age and arthritis, and I don't have to look so gorgeous, and my socks don't match and it's ok because I'm old. I'm over the hill. I run out like a kid – like a child I knew running through the Chicago streets – androgynous me – no earrings, no makeup, no time to mix and match – there's the day, my time, my life. I'm running, I'm going, I'm living. And I'm resting. I'm watching clouds skittering across my skylights; I lie on my couch for hours; my past and my future converge in clouds and flowers outside my window. I'm over the hill. Hello to feeling sad and old and abandoned. Hello to freedom and irritation with all the bullshit and lies: don't put me on, I've been put on all my life and I'm sick and tired of it. Don't say this and mean that, I see through you. Don't put me on hold and don't play Muzak; baby I've had it. Hello to total honesty every instant of my changing mind and world, my glorious bounty, my joy and my pain, my life.

And yes, the hill is large – looming on the horizon, craggy tree stumps and huge rocks to fall on. I've trudged up and slid down and trudged up again and perhaps I'm really over on the other side where it's greener and grassier; the grass is taller, the water is warmer. The rough angles of the climb are slowly receding, I hardly remember them. All the sharp edges are in the past. I'm here, over the hill, falling, tumbling, rolling over, lying on my back in the sun, looking at the sky. Something has gone for sure. Is this what I was so afraid of? This here? This now? I sit and meditate. Let me abide in well-being and peace. Let me abide. My back is straight, my head is firm, my eyes are still. There is no hill, there is no over it, there is only breath, in and out, and the silence, like a gong.

*Bobby Markels*

# Coming to Tea

She was coming to tea. My old friend was a big success now, a famous writer. I didn't have a bag or a leaf in the house. Standing in the store I am amazed at the number of teas available. I read the declarations and promises written on the boxes. I finally choose one, uncertain...

The water is boiling. The little cakes are on the plate. The doorbell rings. Before she gets her coat off she is talking. "Some bastard backed into my rented car right in front of the hotel this morning..."

(Maybe I should be serving Good Mood Tea, with the St. John's Wort.)

She declines the milk and pushes the French sugar cubes aside still talking. "Well, it's nice to see I'm not the only one getting gray, though I continue to bleed like a stuck hog!..."

(Maybe I should be serving Women's Liberty with extra Yam Root.)

She bites into a little strawberry and cream cake, pauses for a moment. Then goes on talking. "Did I tell you I have a new lover, he's British and quite rich..."

(Maybe I should be serving Earl Gray, a delicately scented aristocratic blend.)

She opens the glass Bee container flipping up his silver wings. She dribbles honey into her cup. All the time talking. "Life is good, I'm not actually seeking excitement any more..."

(Maybe I should be serving Jasmine, a calming brew.)

She licks her fingers while talking.

(I realize I am serving the perfect tea – Constant Comment.)

*Sandra Kazanjian*

# Persimmon Bread

PREHEAT OVEN TO 350          MAKES ONE LOAF

3 very ripe persimmons
2 eggs
Sugar
Salt
Olive or other cooking oil
Water
Whole wheat pastry flour
Baking soda
Baking powder
Spices: cinnamon, nutmeg, clove, ginger
Fruits and Nuts: currants or raisins and walnuts

Using some kind of sieve or colander, squish out the pulp from the skins. There should be about 1 cup of pulp to scoop into your mixing bowl. Add the eggs, and mix until smooth. Add 1 3/4 cup sugar (I usually use 3/4 brown sugar, but it can be all white) and a pinch of salt and mix some more.

Now add 1/3 cup of oil and 1/3 cup of water and blend in.

Then add 1 teaspoon soda, and 1/4 teaspoon baking powder to 1 2/3 cup of flour. Add all this into the persimmon mixture and blend until smooth, adding spices to taste.

Last, add 1 cup of nuts and 1 cup of currants.

Mix gently until everything is blended, and pour into a greased 4" x 9" bread pan.

Bake at 350 for about one hour. Let cool, then invert to remove it from the pan and serve plain or with whipped cream. Oh, and don't forget a hot cup of tea.

*Marylu Downing*

# Mr. G.

You hold me to you like a cup in its saucer

Gravity plays a part

The economics of love have nothing to do with finance

The wealth of a heart account is measured in beats;

Each a resource well spent.

I met you on Martin Luther King's birthday

I thought you were a bum. You were a spendthrift.

I took a calculated risk and three shots of tequila

The only alcohol in nine months pregnancy...

Now my daughter studies flamenco

Twenty-three years gone. Where did they go?

Sometimes this cup is half empty

Would you top it up with a little cream

For old times' sake?

Never mind the nostalgia

A nap on the warm sandy beach of time

And your gray-blue eyes are just

My cup of tea.

*Meryl Krause*

# A Hint of Almond

*H*er aunt was finicky about her tea. She favored a strong tea, a blend of Chinese black orchid flavored Keemun and Black Dragon, an Oolong tea grown in Taiwan, dark and tasting of peach blossoms. Brewing the perfect cup of tea was an art, and more than once she had suffered the wrath of her aunt's dissatisfaction and had been sent back to the kitchen to "get it right this time."

Surprisingly, she had begun to enjoy the challenge. If she delivered a cup of tea and got a curt nod of dismissal she knew she had been successful. Lately, she had begun experimenting by adding a few leaves from different varieties: Jade Oolong with its sweet smooth taste, a few leaves of Anqi Oolong, for its astringent flavor. Her aunt seemed to approve, although she was as ungracious as ever and never said thank you.

She prepared this afternoon's tea with extra care, steeping the fragrant leaves until they turned the water a golden brown. She poured herself a cup before measuring and stirring a special ingredient into her aunt's tea. A touch of white powder, which she suspected was quite deadly. It dissolved in the brown liquid without a trace. She smelled the heady aroma, blending the flavors of orchid and peach blossom with just a hint of almond.

She opened the door to the parlor slowly so as not to upset the tea tray. Her aunt, fastidious in gray silk, waited impatiently as the tea was poured. She watched her aunt's sour face as she took the first sip, watched as her lips tightened and then relaxed. She was dismissed with a brusque nod.

Back in the kitchen she sat close to the fire and sipped her tea. It was remarkable the satisfaction she felt from making her aunt a perfect cup of tea.

*Marilyn B. Kinghorn*

# Tea Leaves

She hadn't noticed anything at first of course, but then she was a small child, eight or nine at the time. She did remember one comment of her parents, drifting back to her over the front seat of the huge old Dodge as they were driving home at night. She had been looking up at the streetlights, counting them as they flashed by. "Hon, do you see any lights?" her father had asked her mother. She couldn't hear her mother's response, but she peered out the window and saw a lamp on the light post flicker out when they drove by, and so did the next one. She turned around peering out the elliptical back window, and noticed that it turned on again. The next one did it too, and then the next. She counted eighty-five total.

She was twelve, and having her first tea ever. Her mother pushed the cup across the polished wood surface of the table to her. She carefully lifted the cup so it wouldn't spill and sipped. She looked up at her mother to see her staring intently back at her. Some people described them as mirror images, with the same curly brown hair, the same dark brown eyes with heavy brown eyelashes, and the same bow-shaped tiny mouths. She thought that the tea was delicious.

Lifting the cup again, she saw the bottom was filled with leaves, and she had to wait for the leaves to settle before she drank the tea. "Swirl the leaves at the bottom dear," her mother mildly suggested. She swirled the leaves, and as the kaleidoscope of leaves settled into a pattern, she saw something, like a picture show. Startled, she pushed away the teacup as if it were about to explode. Her mother nodded.

That's when she confirmed her gift of "sight" and when she decided never ever to drink a cup of tea again. Not even with a tea bag – it could break!

*Mimi Luebbermann*

# Root Cellar

*I* want a root cellar,

a deep, dark root cellar

with a dry, sanded floor.

I want my root cellar filled with knobby shapes:

bitter tang of raw rutabagas,

sweet grain of turnips,

hardness of parsnips...

potent shapes with earth still clinging to them.

I want a root cellar

so all the roots can reveal their mysteries,

so they can yield up lost dreams

to invading teeth,

so the roots can return all the lost dreams of summer

that slipped into the ground as the sun rose.

The dreams of summer could feed me all winter long

if I had a root cellar.

*Andrea Granahan*

# Thousand Faces of Buddha

Abundance is sitting in the center of translucent rainbows
    Surrounded by a thousand faces of Buddha

Its meaning is felt when our cup is empty
Our lives can be richly filled even after our cup breaks
Spilling its old ideas and dreams into the saucer

We inherit new cups for our collection
Filling us up with courage and inspiring fresh hope
Symbolic scenes, sometimes literal or floral
Trusting in the rich nature of Self
Delicately held and finely balanced

Choose your cup! We need never drink alone
Our lives are revealed and mirrored
In a circle of tea-time sharings
Are we honest and kind?
Do we have friends who will stay with us in intimate embrace?
Do we laugh many times each day?
Are we gracious as
The invisible Creator
Replenishes our cup again and again?

Our cups may be placed on lace tablecloths, wood or dirt
Remember, life abounds in mysterious quantities
Given gratitude and abundance
Mindfully consume life's constant and endless refills

*Janelle Va Melvin*

# The Kingdom of Teacups

For my mother and her friends, teacups have always been the traditional engagement gift. When my own nuptials were announced twenty years ago, they sent nearly a dozen hand-painted delicacies, packed like eggs in elegantly wrapped boxes.

At first I was somewhat puzzled by gifts which celebrated my marriage but clearly excluded my mate. These were not vessels designed to accommodate his virile paws and wide, eager mouth. But later, at the lavish bridal showers, as tea steamed in cups from their own collections, I realized that these women were inducting me into the Society of Wives. I took it as a sign that one day I, too, would be expected to hold court in an exclusively feminine kingdom of linen, crystal, dainty china, silver flatware. I found this taste of the future slightly fusty, even alarming. I joked with my unmarried girlfriends about forsaking my husband for gossip and bridge.

I didn't know much about marriage then, enamored as I was with the prospect of one-ness. I couldn't know that even with a strong, fiercely protective husband, women would be the ones to save my life again and again. Over the years, I have discovered the healing powers of tea poured into fluted porcelain and placed before a grieving friend, how the clinking of cups against saucers strengthens a woman's laughter, works charms against despair. My mother's friends, who were at the age I am now, knew there are celebrations and sorrows we wives must weather. In the kingdoms we build of teacups, there is community and shelter.

*Susan Bono*

# Long Shadows

The long shadows of World War II had not quite reached Portland, Oregon in the summer of 1941. At twelve I was experiencing uncommon freedoms. I could ride my blue Schwinn with its silver fenders down the long stretch of Thirty-third Street to Columbia Boulevard and the Japanese truck farms where my friends Tommy and Kiko Hasagawa lived.

All summer we rode our bikes together. In the fall we stopped to warm our hands at the antique ceramic hibachi behind their shed and drink the hot, green tea that Mrs. Hasagawa brewed and served in simple cups with no handles and tiny lids.

Then, one winter morning, my father announced that our usual Saturday shopping at the truck farms would be postponed indefinitely. The Hasagawas were gone.

"Where did they go?" I asked. I knew that Japan had bombed Pearl Harbor. I knew about the Japanese internment camps and that the government had rounded up Japanese like common criminals and loaded them on trains and buses and sent them away. But Tommy and Kiko?

"Where did they take Tommy and Kiko?" I begged my father.

"I don't know," he answered carefully. "Somewhere safe. The Japanese killed many of our men, and people are very angry. It's for their own good, you know; we wouldn't want something terrible to happen to them."

"But why did they take my friends?" I keened, the question trailing us that cold winter morning, hanging blood red against the gray sky.

*Sara Spaulding-Phillips*

# His Gift

Today I am an honored guest. I feel this with each step I take on the narrow path carpeted with mosses. I sit on the bench in the waiting-arbor (*machiai*) of the outer tea garden (*roji*), tall clumps of bamboo on either side. The morning light is muted, shaded by trees. The green roji conveys a sense of safety and transition. I'm calm, and breathe deeply.

The muffled sound of his sandals on the stones signals the arrival of my esteemed host. He smiles and bows. I follow him through another bamboo gate into the inner garden. I gaze around, feeling the peace and emptying-out that the "pond" of smooth stones suggests. I approach the stone water basin (*tsukubai*), lift the bamboo dipper, and carefully, ritualistically, rinse my hands, my mouth and finally, the handle of the dipper.

We ascend the steps to the teahouse, remove our shoes, and pull on clean socks. The doorway is so small we must crawl through on hands and knees. The tea garden has left me serene, more conscious of my body. I surprise myself with something that approaches grace in a very awkward and humbling maneuver. Entering, I notice the softly lit alcove with a Japanese scroll and a single, very beautiful flower in a small vase. I pause, deeply appreciating its beauty and balance. I bow to my host and he to me. He explains the meaning of the scroll: "Fame and Profit are put to rest, All is Impermanence".

We kneel for preparation of the tea. My host, in what seems a beautifully choreographed ballet, silently and gracefully displays the finely wrought, immaculate utensils he will use. He has selected an ivory-glazed, raku tea bowl made in the wabi/sabi tradition. He presents the open canister of green tea for my inspection. The chartreuse powder is richly fragrant. He carefully scoops it into my tea bowl, and adds boiling water. His split bamboo whisk (*chasen*) whips the powder until it's a frothy green. When he is convinced that the tea is perfect, he carefully presents it.

It nourishes me immediately and in so many ways. After finishing the very last drop, I bow deeply, with gratitude beyond words.

*Kathleen Willett*

# Irish Magic

My mother drove me from the hospital to Grandma's house. She told me how Grandma's black cat waited for me, and how I could have all the ice cream I wanted, but I sat hunched in silent fury. I was four and she hadn't come to see me at the hospital. She told me later that Dr. Goodhill convinced her not to come because I might cry and damage my surgery. All I knew then was that other parents arrived during visiting hours to wave from behind the glass partition, while I watched and waited.

When we got to Grandma's, my mother acceded at once to my demand for chocolate ice cream. The torture of trying to swallow that ice cream magnified my anger at her, and I refused, from that moment, to eat or drink anything other than ice chips. For days.

I languished in bed, becoming more and more stubborn as my mother became frantic for me to eat. Finally, my Irish grandmother took over. She put her afternoon cuppa on a silver tray and brought it into the bedroom where I was holed up with the cat. She set out her much-admired porcelain teacups, and a pink-flowered bowl of sugar lumps. "Tea," she said, "is the most magical of medicines." I wrinkled my nose. "'Tis even more powerful," she said, "with exactly three lumps of sugar." She handed me the tongs. I whispered the numbers as I dropped in the lumps. "Now we must wait until the sugar is completely dissolved." My defiance melted with the sugar and I drank two whole cups.

Grandma went into the kitchen and fried up a rabbit. She mashed potatoes and heated a can of spinach, all well-known favorites of mine. My mother hovered at the table with Jello and ice cream, convinced I would injure myself swallowing Grandma's rough food. Next to my plate was one of the same lovely teacups, sugar bowl right alongside. I held the tongs and looked up. Grandma gave a quick nod. That meal of rabbit, potatoes, and spinach, punctuated with sharp pain and sweet tea, still lives as one of the best in my life.

*Dee Watt*

# If We Are Lucky

*If* we are lucky, it may be something

Like this: ...driving west into November

Twilight, drawn homeward through familiar hills,

The oaks standing tranced, a branched

Intaglio splayed against a sky that glows

Like ripe fruit. All things seem clear... the chilled

Transparent air, the light that fades along the brink,

Love; fate. We have traveled this way before.

The road twines through the canyon where night pools

And rises. A scatter of starlings spins

Overhead, swept towards its roost in the alders,

Shadow seeps from the thickets along the creek.

One star burns above the blanched horizon.

Now, the road runs uphill, past houses like

Lanterns. From the last ridge, the skyline

Cracks and kindles. We drop down into

Dark. From here on we follow, blind, urged

Towards the loved voice, the lighted doorway.

*Laura Gildart Sauter*

# Monkey Business

On a small plot of land overlooking the village there is an enchanted cemetery the grandchildren call "Monkey City." The name comes from Rudyard Kipling's *Jungle Book*, as it reminds the children of the ancient hidden city that houses an immense treasure of golden coins, chalices, crowns, diamonds, rubies, pearls; gems beyond imagining, all guarded by thousands of monkeys.

The children run freely, fascinated with everything: a shell necklace glued to a headstone, a rhinestone heart swaying from a rose bush, the carved angels and tiny statues of the Virgin Mary, the huge marble crosses, the silk flowers. On one grave there are helium Happy Birthday balloons, a bouquet of sunflowers, a tiny stuffed bear and two white ceramic rabbits clustered around a photo of a small child.

Their grandmother sleeps in the shade of a veiled monument as they swoop and soar noiselessly like little glider planes dancing with the spirits. They revel in the silence, the heat of the sun, until tired at last they lay on their backs against a cool marble gravestone and watch the clouds form piglets and elephants in the sky.

*Salli Rasberry*

# Morning

*I*t was cold in the kitchen. She clicked on the electric teapot to boil water and built a fire in the wood stove. Outside, one of the four roosters started crowing. She stood at the door looking out at the lightening sky in the east, and the silhouettes of the oak trees, flat black shapes with fringed fan tops perching on the horizon line, and one, her favorite, akimbo on top of the hill that blocked her view of the rising sun.

She cupped the sludge, what she called her first cup of tea, in her hands. The first cup thickened with four teaspoons, generous, of sugar, and a slug of half-and-half. At five in the morning, she needed the jolt, and the tea soup tasted delicious and warmed her body. The mug was one she found in a flea market, and it pictured a castle in Ethiopia.

She thought of the tea parties with Aunt Anne at Grandmother McMillan's house. Aunt Anne had started the tea parties because her elderly mother wasn't able to get out. Grandmother had presided at the head of the table, her white hair a flaring nimbus around her face, while she and Aunt Anne ran around the long table in the kitchen renewing the teapot and buttering slices of toast. Everyone talked, interrupted, teased, cajoled, with laughter and stories and shining happy faces until at last, when the toast plates held only crumbs, and the mugs only leaves, the guests reluctantly pushed back their chairs.

She remembered Grandmother sitting in the kitchen as they cleaned up, chuckling and laughing at stories and jokes her friends had shared. As Aunt Anne walked Grandmother back to her room for a rest, she could hear them still talking over the day's tea party as she let herself out the back door.

With a shake and a sigh, she brought herself back to the present. Grandmother had been dead over thirty years. With a start she realized she herself was about Aunt Anne's age that summer of the tea parties. Looking out at the far Antonio Mountain, she saw that the first rays of soft orange sunlight had lit the topmost dome. Reluctantly putting down her teacup, she went to get her coat. It was time to start her day.

*Mimi Luebbermann*

# My Loving Will Rock You Forever

She was looking for the door to his soul. That door had closed a little over two years ago and it had become more and more hidden as time passed. Before, he had been bright, sunny... eyes a Siamese cat blue, hair white and soft. His very presence had brought joy into her life.

Now he sat on the cool green and white tiles of the kitchen floor, rocking back and forth, back and forth, sliding a turquoise Melamine plate under his left hand. Whether she spoke to him, or not; whether she sang to him, or not; whether she sat with him, or not; he rocked back and forth, sliding the plate.

Sometimes, he would allow her to hold him on her lap-as long as she rocked him. When she was holding him, she would look into his eyes, searching for the boy she had once known. Behind those blue-sky eyes, a cloud, and behind it, she assumed, was a closed door.

Today they would celebrate his fourth birthday. "We'll have dinner on the sunny patio, which he won't eat much of," she thought, "and a cake, whose candles he won't blow out." For a moment she wondered, "What's the point?"

"The point is to love him as he is; if there is a way to open the door, it has to be through loving him."

She reached down and touched him-he didn't pull away. She sat down behind him with her legs wide, their bodies barely touching and, rocking in his rhythm, she recited her song of love to him:

"I love you, my beautiful boy
my beautiful blue-eyed boy
my loving will rock you forever...
whether you come out or stay in
I will love you and rock you forever."

*Fran Simon*

70

# Laughter

*I* studied laughter with my grandmother
making candy
licking
the bowl
tickling her waist
as she leaned over
the pot
her hand firm
holding a spoon
stuck with a sticky
ball
newly formed sugar, butter,
as if it would last forever.

*Jane K. Stuppin*

## What I Took to the Hospital

FIFTEEN MINUTES AFTER

Being told the lump didn't look like a fibroid – shivering with shock – I wrote. . .

Feeling my feelings of shock and surprise,

Of how much I love my life,

How much I want to live,

How much I cherish being healthy, vital and active.

Of course, I feel shaken to the core.

Welcome to the human race.

WHAT I TOOK TO THE HOSPITAL

Bright pink squishy earplugs.

Eye covers for sleeping.

Lots of pictures of people and animals I love.

A small teddy bear in green corduroy overalls.

A few talismans, amulets and rocks

from people and places that I love.

My own toothpaste.

Affirmations and prayers

which I asked friends or visitors to read to me aloud

twice each day.

AFFIRMATION

Earth, I kiss you with my feet.

Water, how I love to feel the way you clean me.

Air, fresh, renewing my life moment by moment.

Fire, the spirit of life in every holy cell.

Blessed be my body.

Vessel of my soul.

Sacred territory of the mystery of being born in a body.

*Annie Kavanagh*

# Summer

The whole day was to be used.
Mornings
we woke.
Daily scrambles to the garden
daily discoveries; the cucumbers
were larger, the strawberries redder.

Afternoons
Tea parties in the back yard.
Teapots filled with water.
Teacups matching saucers.
Tea cakes, imagined.
Even our brothers
barefoot and shirtless
when invited to tea, behaved.

Nighttimes
on our beds, eyes wide open,
we shouted whispers to each other.

It was the summer that connected
day to day.
Then we slept.
Not having known the name of that day
or the name of the tomorrows to come.

*Glory Leifried*

# Jonathan

You were conceived on the fifth day
   of my mother's death, when I took your father
   into my body, praying for her to come back.

   Every night I dreamt she was alive,
   young and elegant, every glorious morning
   was her death again. And through the days of tears

   down San Francisco hills, you continued
   to swim through me until the day of labor,
   when I lost too much blood, when you

   lost your heart beat. They had to pull
   you out with metal hands, umbilical rope
   around your neck, no vital signs. By then

   I knew you, the moment before all went black,
   we were in front each other. I gave you
   all I needed to give you in this whole life,

   let you go, knowing what life knows,
   and you came back, they laid you on me,
   bloody and breathing on my breast.

*Carmen Castillo*

# Memoir from South Africa

They were delicate with flowers on them, but not expensive delicate fine English China. Those were for wealthy households. Tea was served on the lawn, on hot summer days, when we lazily sat under the weeping willow tree, awaiting the presentation of the tray, white tea towel, and assorted biscuits.

And tea was served on the day of the Poquos.

The Poquos were eighteen black men charged with high treason, an offense for which they would be hanged if found guilty. My father, a lawyer, had agreed to defend the Poquo Gang.

All eighteen men arrived at once and walked solemnly up our driveway, resembling a column attending a funeral. In those insane days of apartheid, there was something terrifying about this event. Dad was known for his generous eccentricity. He met with the group, arranged in a circle of chairs on the tenequoit court.

They all wore dark suits, white shirts with ties, and hats, a kind of saboteur's uniform, and sat politely in a circle while Dad took their brief. Katy, the cook, arrived with the tea tray carefully arranged with cups, saucers, milk jug and sugar bowl, on a white tea towel, and somberly poured. As each cup was offered, so was the milk and sugar.

I sat in the Chinese guava tree, an eleven-year-old girl, watching, wondering about these men and my father, who, in spite of apartheid, had kept his humanity intact.

*Margaret Caminsky-Shapiro*

## Seventeen

*I* remember the sweet cedar smell,
  Raw emotions of love and hate,
  Row of tulips carved on top –
  Childhood in a rectangular box.

  They presumed I would adore it,
  Just like the amber pearls,
  Girlish and ordered neat on a string,
  Refusing even the promise of wildness.

  But a dream that night disturbed my peace.
  From a manicured lawn green with gratitude,
  Out popped those gifts,
  Larger than life on long coiled springs.

  Soon a man and I were almost lovers
  With a necklace he had threaded himself,
  Rough red beads to rouse my sensibilities
  Against a turquoise center.

  He placed the beads around my neck
  Kissing the nape,
  My reflection in the darkened window
  A woman leaving home.

*Mella Mincberg*

# Her Blush

My 87-year-old aunt Thea's hands could barely hold her cup with pink peonies and green vines, but as she sipped, color rose in her cheeks, and in a surprisingly clear voice, she told me about buying the tea set in Hong Kong in 1938.

China was already engulfed in war. The Japanese occupied Nanking, Shanghai, Canton. Hong Kong would be next but until then the British were having a moveable party, dancing until dawn, riding a funicular up Tiger Hill to watch sunrise spatter gold over the bays. One night, on a floating river restaurant, a handsome English banker approached her table and asked her to dance. Thea wore a midnight blue silk with a close-fitting waist and bias-cut skirt. She loved pretty clothes with the passion of a girl given hand-me-downs during the Depression. The next morning the Englishman sent the visiting American two-dozen roses.

In this intense time, they fell in love, went exploring shops, buying her fine china, dancing cheek to cheek. He wore a gardenia in his lapel. She wore *L'Heure Bleue*-cinnamon and carnations. She didn't tell me outright about sex, but as memory painted her cheeks, I revised a long-held image of my "maiden" aunt Thea.

With the last taste of tea, fragrances of flowers in the Tiger Balm gardens, her own perfume in the tropical air, the lover who disappeared forever, slipped away. She held the cup's delicate handle between her fingers, the final essence on her lips.

*Barbara L. Baer*

## Coleman Valley Road to the Coast

*I* sit and wonder why I like to eat

    stars for breakfast,

    clouds with tea

    and dessert on the moon.

Though my interplanetary itinerary doesn't

    include Pluto or Saturn,

    Mercury is fascinating and

    I always long for Venus.

But an Earthly picnic is so bountiful and rich

    No other place offers

    such sensual treats as the scent of

    Eucalyptus leaves

On the way to crashing ocean waves, the

    smoothness of sea-polished rocks on my back,

    the warmth from the touch of human skin

    and the beauty of a single kiss.

*Meryl Krause*

## A Circle of Memories

One of my first memories is having a tea party with my mom. She pulled a chair up to the kitchen counter for me and I made sugar-water tea, while she did the dishes. I was about two years old.

Until I was six, tea parties were a favorite playtime for me. For the next dozen years or so, I lost interest in tea parties. Then, as a college student, I spent a lot of time philosophizing with friends or just plain gossiping. Sipping on a cup of tea seemed to make our conversations more inspiring.

As a married woman my husband and I would sit in the "talking chairs" each evening, relaxing with our bedtime tea as we worked out the details of our life. I have just given my two-year-old daughter a tea set, and I'm looking forward to having her make sugar-water tea next to me while I do the dishes.

*Jean Martinelli*

# Shamrocks

My husband and I recently traveled to Ireland. For us, the trip was a dream come true, though in different ways. He is Irish and wanted to draw closer to his heritage. I am battling cancer. For me, travel is life.

The only thing I really wanted to buy was a teapot and teacups. Wherever our tour bus stopped, I combed the shops. In a little store near the Blarney Castle, I saw my teapot and teacup sitting on the shelf. It was a beautiful teapot, so dainty and sweet, a cream color with little green shamrocks. I knew it was the one for me and had it shipped home.

From the day my teapot arrived, I became the Tea Party Queen. I gave parties for my nurses, birthday tea parties, tea parties for friends. I lit candles on our tables and served scones, lemon curd, raspberry jam and clotted cream. We ate delicate sandwiches on paper doilies and listened to music.

Drinking from the teacups has become another symbol of life for me. Everyone's life is brewed with different blends and strengths. I take my shamrock teacup wherever I go now as a constant companion. Sometimes I burn my special candle in it. My teacup represents all the love in my life that fills my cup.

*Christine Musso-Truax*

## Winter Violets

*I* pour tea after the rest of the house goes dark. I sit on my blue couch and look out the window and the one who looks like me stares back. In the wet reflection I am my mother, a resemblance which startled me the first time, like a haunting. But now, I welcome it and imagine that a part of her has come for tea.

I use her teapot, a slender vessel with wisteria blossoms and a gold handle that she bought at an auction in Florida, when she thought she'd be happy there. This flowered cup she drank out of for years. It's covered with violets, as determinedly cheerful as the ones she pinned to her winter coat on cold March days in Pennsylvania. A thin crack runs down the inside of the cup, like a brown vein and there's a chip in the rim. My lip seeks the chip that hers once touched just as my eyes seek hers in the window. I think what I might tell her to make her laugh. Finally, we have time for each other, every night, if we want.

*Susan Swartz*

## Just a Woman and a Garden

She imagines men,
　　lords and healers. Wind
　　flows through her fingers.
　　When she talks to her garden,

　　the chard ripples, each stem glows
　　like a handful of garnets, fat rubies.
　　She answers the black-headed grosbeaks,
　　screams with ravens. Sometimes

　　she thinks of Utah.
　　Sunset on the Orange Cliffs,
　　each edge defined. In her dreams
　　she is always bare-breasted

　　at a party, in the checkout line.
　　Everyone else wears clothes.
　　She hugs groceries to her chest.
　　Maybe no one will notice.

　　She has nothing to sell,
　　not even
　　for too low a price.
　　She has everything.

*Liza Prunuske*

# Pilgrimage to Katmandu

Following an auspicious pilgrimage to Bhutan, we arrive in Nepal. Our mission is to deliver a package of sacred teachings to a holy woman, and with luck we find her. Grateful to receive the gift, she invites us to join in a ritual celebrating the passing of a great Sherpa Lama of her lineage. After a cup of tea, we enter the monastery, a huge stone building smelling of incense and softly lit with candles.

A stage is being built while monks practice ritual dances. Men, women, and a few children are cleaning, chanting, preparing food and making a special fire which must last for three days of cooking and making tea.

The Lamas are hungry for our stories of Bhutan where we participated in rituals for the recently deceased Dilgo Khyentse, Rinpoche, teacher of the Dali Lama. Sitting on cushions, drinking homemade Sherpa beer, our conversation is translated by a Tibetan friend.

We spend the next three days with the gentle, rugged Sherpa people. We watch the stage transform into an altar where continuous rituals are performed, offerings made. Chanting, singing, horns, bells and blessings permeate the space. The wife of the deceased Lama holds my hand and gazes lovingly into my soul. It's a sacred time. We alternate walking, eating, chanting and sitting in meditation. Hot cups of tea appear in front of us. The cups warm our hands. As I sip the smoke-flavored black tea, I feel my cells expand beyond my body and my mind expand beyond the universe.

*Ellen Galford*

# Rooted in Both Directions

Deeply bound in rocky earth
   roots twine down.
   The pull of gravity
   against vast, airy heavens.

We're always rooted in both directions
   the here and now
   and whatever comes next.

Like shrouded caterpillars,
   we will metamorphose,
   leaving our earthly cocoons
   for the unknown.

Some say death is white and welcoming.
   Maybe it's hot, and bright vermilion.
   Or, cloaked in the soft peace
   of dark nothingness.

I imagine my garden, heat of a summer's day,
   light freedom of flying above
   leafy green, red pineapple sage,
   lavender stalks, white rose petals.

Slow tumbling change on a light wind,
   shiny small thistle seed drifting up and out.
   A changeling, looking back only once.
   Gone, off in another direction.

*Marylu Downing*

# Winter Dancing

Inky apple trees etched against the evening sky
do a winter dance, all elbows, crooked fingers
and Ichabod knees. In rows of silent abandon,
they celebrate ecstatic otherness.

Their rough angles jut and poke
through my thin skin. My feet stick and sink
to root in the boggy hill, ankles all knobs,
hips too, and spine, and cervical,
and through me a dark sap rises
toward the bright cup of moonlight and those migrant clouds crossing the
border in darkness
while the houses hold their phantom flicker lives.

My old bones grow green inside, lifting and bending
under bark black with ancient fire, wet black
twisted branches, forgotten after pruning –
leafless, fruitless, grown joyous,
wearing only the wind, the fine gauze
of this light rain.

*Elizabeth Carothers Herron*

# Reverberation

In time

all that I have done,

all that I have lived,

will be forgotten.

But there is that within me

which says it is important

that I cherish my existence,

as it is the essence of that love

which will reverberate

even when I am gone.

*Annie Kavanagh*

**Barbara L. Baer** lives in Forestville, California, writes a little of everything, long and short fiction, essays, reviews for regional and national publications. She started Floreant Press in 1995 to publish women's regional writing.

**Robin Beeman**'s latest work of fiction is *The Lost Art of Desire*. She prefers Irish Breakfast tea, brewed strong, with milk and sugar.

**Susan Bono** writes, teaches and edits from her office in Petaluma, California. She has been publishing *Tiny Lights*, a journal of personal essay since 1995. Find out more at www.tiny-lights.com.

**Laura Bulkin** was born in New York and escaped in 1993. She is currently writing a television show in Taos, New Mexico.

**Margaret Caminsky-Shapiro** placed her pen onto the thin blue lines to reveal an eccentric and dramatic South African childhood, an orthodox Eastern European ancestry and a Northern California awakening.

**Carmen Castillo**'s poems have appeared in *Lyric*, *The Squaw Review*, the *Dry Creek Review*, *The Dickens* and other publications. She lives in Santa Rosa, California with her husband and two children.

**Terry Ehret** is a poet, teacher, and publisher. Her works include *Suspension, Lost Body*, and most recently, *Translations from the Human Language*. She lives and teaches in Sonoma County, California.

**Sarah Flowers** ... off the grid and out of the loop, her poems have been in 30 publications in the USA and Ireland.

**Mary Gaffney**'s writing has been published by Floreant Press, and in *Tiny Lights, The Dickens* and numerous *Travelers' Tales* anthologies.

**Andrea Granahan**, from the wilds of Alabama, is well-traveled and makes her home in a forest in Northern California. She is a retired journalist and now devotes her time to travel writing and poetry.

**Elizabeth Carothers Herron**, poet, fiction writer, and essayist, teaches, writes and lives in Paradise – shhhhhh – she means Sonoma County, California.

**Annie Kavanagh**, in remission from ovarian cancer, is dedicated to well-being, promoting nutrition and healthy products, and being in the moment. Her healing journal is posted at http://users.iglide.net/anniek/anniessong.html.

**Sandra Kazanjian**, writer and sculptor, lives in an apple orchard with a spotted dog.

**Marilyn B. Kinghorn** writes, teaches, takes long walks, has two wonderful daughters and makes her home in Forestville, California with husband, David, and an aging army of dogs and cats.

**Meryl Krause** studies herbal medicine in Australia, when she is not at home writing poetry in Occidental, California.

**Lori Kuwabara**, a native Californian *sansei*, lives in Berkeley, California where she's working on an ever-elusive book of short stories. Her favorite tea at the moment is jasmine green. *Namaste*.

**Glory Liefried** has lived in Sonoma County, California, all her life, except for a brief period in Germany. Glory is a mother, preschool teacher, and a student interested in the issues that concern people of color.

**Jane Holly Love** is the author events coordinator for a Northern California independent bookstore. Among her personal essays, a new one about a beleaguered river in the Ohio Valley will soon be published by *Pig Iron*.

**Mimi Luebbermann** lives and works on *Wind Rush,* her small farm outside Petaluma, California, farming and gardening sustainably with Jersey cows, fine wool sheep, chickens, llamas, alpacas, rabbits, cats and dogs.

**Bobby Markels**, Mendocino, California resident since 1966, is known for her one-woman shows. She is the author of five books, and her many articles, stories and poems have appeared in magazines.

**Jean Martinelli**, lifelong Michigan resident, is a 50-year-old wife, mother and teacher. Growing up the 6th of 10 children, she was encouraged to be a writer.

**Janelle Va Melvin** has spent the last 15 years in the Valley of the Moon as a hospice midwife and chaplain. She co-directs a nonprofit organization, Final Passages, dedicated to a personalized home funeral experience.

**Mella Mincberg** loves solitude and family life, forests and beaches, classical and folk-rock guitar music, prose and poetry. She lives with her husband and daughter in Sebastopol, California, where she is at work on a novel.

**Christine Musso-Truax** lives in Santa Rosa, California with her husband. She survives and thrives by living in the moment.

**Fionna Perkins** "The accounting is not where I've been but where I am at the moment – alive and doing more than just breathing."

**Liza Prunuske** is a lover of wild birds. She lives with her family in the hills west of Occidental, California.

**Salli Rasberry**, creator of the Coffin Garden, author of *The Art of Dying, Honoring and Celebrating Life's Passages*, and many other social change books, is currently passionate about her new company, Shrinedesign.com.

**Anne Regan** tries to give as much time as she can to her writing, but her son Skyler is her main topic at the moment; he is three years old.

**Clara Rosemarda**, writer, counselor, and creative writing teacher, swims in the world of words as in the Russian River. She sees creativity not as a luxury, but a necessity.

**Laura Gildart Sauter's** poems, short stories and essays have appeared in *Loon, The Dickens, Tiny Lights, Convolvulous, Dark Hollow* and the *Sow's Ear Review*. She is the recipient of the *Sow's Ear Review* poetry prize.

**Fran Simon** finally stepped out of the closet as a writer in the early 90s. A gypsy at heart, she is currently residing near Taos, New Mexico, where she is gestating two books.

**Sara Spaulding-Phillips**, word lover, writer, artist, recovering psychotherapist, teaches creative writing. She has been published in *Sacred Heritage; The Influence of Shamanism on Analytical Psychology*, and many anthologies.

**Jane K. Stuppin** writes short stories and poetry. Her work has been published in literary journals and broadcast on PBS radio. She is currently in an MFA writing program.

**Susan Swartz** is a newspaper columnist and author of *Juicy Tomatoes: Plain Truths, Dumb Lies and Sisterly Advice About Life After 50,* New Harbinger Publications, 2000.

**Dee Watt** is a marriage and family therapist in Santa Rosa, California and a dedicated dressage rider.

**Kathleen Willett** loves Japanese gardens, *matcha* tea, nature, the arts, and the man she lives with. This is her second publication.

# Acknowledgments

For their support and belief in our book, we wish to thank our husbands, Roger House, Dennis Galford, and Pat Murphy.

Thanks to friends who loaned teacups and accessories from their collections, Anna Ransome, Janelle Va Melvin, Verna Melvin, Annie Kavanagh, Joseph Williams, Michael Krafu, and Margaret Detwiler. For loaning various tea items, thanks to Occidental's Forget Me Not, Freestone's Enduring Comfort and Sebastopol's The Irish Shop. And for their display from the Graton Flower Show accompanying *His Gift*, thanks to Nancy Kesselring and Dale Jewell.

We thank artists Barbara Hoffman, whose cup and teapot grace *Elixir of the Ages,* and whose cup accompanies *Summer*; Sherry Van Gelder, whose goddess sculpture (next to Marylu's mosaic pot), accompanies *Just a Woman and a Garden*, and whose fish raku we used for *Coleman Valley Road to the Coast*. Faith Morgan sculpted the pregnant torso which accompanies *MacKenzie,* and created the pot used for *Summer.*

Bob Bingenheimer used his graphic design skill to bring it all together. Barbara L. Baer, Robin Beeman, Dee Watt, Anne Regan and Roger House read the written materials. Aubri Lane patiently photographed us for the back flap, and John Morgan of Raven Rock Press spent hours scanning and color-correcting to ensure the quality of the photographs. The tea companies listed in the directory gave information, and supplied the tea for our readings. Special thanks to Julie Baron from Taylor Maid Farms, Emma Mann from Traditional Medicinals and to Suzanne Baird from TAZO Tea, for their participation in our "tea parties."

We want to acknowledge the many bookstores that sponsor readings and "tea parties" for the book; special thanks to Jane Love of Copperfield's Books. Barbara L. Baer of Floreant Press and Sue Pekarsky Gary of Garmento Speak supplied their self-publication expertise. Lynne Dennis of TWP America helped get the book printed. Thanks to Fionna Perkins for telling us about Monkey Pluck*,* and to *The Thousand Recipe Chinese Cookbook* by Gloria Bley Miller which Fionna mentions in her piece, *First Date.* We also acknowledge the Union Hotel Bakery for a congenial meeting space and delicious apricot-raspberry turnovers.

*Marylu Downing, Ellen Galford and Faith Morgan, 2002*

If you are looking for just the right tea, special tea accessories, more information about tea, or even a place to drink tea, try the tea providers below:

1. **Alltea.com** is an online tea market with over 25 gourmet brands of popular black, green, oolong, rooibos, chai, and herbal teas, as well as bulk teas, teapots, kettles, assorted teaware and gifts. Online at www.alltea.com

2. **Far Leaves** is a tea salon in Berkeley, California located at 2979 College Ave. (at Ashby Ave.) whose specialty is green teas from China, Taiwan and Japan. In addition, they carry herbal, flavored and nutritional teas. Online at www.farleaves.com or phone 510-665-9409.

3. **Peet's Coffee and Tea** offers over 35 varieties of the finest, freshest, hand-selected teas sourced from the top producers in the world. In addition to its regular menu, Peet's offers rare teas available in very limited quantities. For information or to order, visit www.peets.com or call 800-999-2132.

4. **Rishi Tea,** importer of premium loose-leaf tea, specializes in organic varietals, traveling to Asia's top gardens several times a year to select the best new teas of each season, purchasing small lots directly from farmers. They also offer elegant gift sets, authentic teaware and unique handcrafted herbal blends. More than 80 green, black, white, oolong, pu-erh and herbal teas are available in North American specialty food stores and online at www.rishi-tea.com, or call: 866 RISHI TEA. Three-time winner of SCAA's Best Tea awards.

5. **Taylor Maid Farms,** certified organic coffee roaster and tea blender, offers many colorful, flavorful and aromatic black and green teas and herbal tisanes. Many of the herbs used are grown on their farm in western Sonoma County, California. Wholesale/retail outlet store, mail order, online at www.taylormaidfarms.com or by phone: 707-824-9110. Located at 6793 McKinley Ave., Sebastopol, CA 95472.

6. **TAZO** creates premium full leaf teas, filter bag teas, chai and bottled iced and juiced teas. On the Internet at TAZO.com, or by phone: 800-299-9445, Portland, OR.

7. **TEAHOUSE Magazine** is a Northern California quarterly which explores the world's tea traditions and innovations, and celebrates the many ways that tea brings people together. All enjoyment, no dogma. TEAHOUSE Magazine, P.O. Box 1135, Pinole, CA 94564, or online at teahousemag@earthlink.net.

8. **Traditional Medicinals** was founded in 1974 with the idea of providing herbal self-care for health-conscious consumers. At first they made tea formulas based on the individual needs of customers – 27 years later they've grown to become the largest medicinal herbal tea manufacturer. They offer a wide selection of herbal teas in unbleached bags available in stores across the nation or online at www.TRADITIONALMEDICINALS.com. They are located at 4515 Ross Rd., Sebatopol, CA 95472.

Looking for More Books?

**Floreant Press:** Women's writing – fiction, essays, memoir, and poetry. To see more Floreant Press books, please visit our website at http://members.aol.com/ floreant/index.html.

**Teacups Group:** To order *Jasmine Nights & Monkey Pluck*, or to order a set of 12 photo image greeting cards, please visit us online at teacupsgroup.com or send an inquiry to Teacups Group, 12655 Fiori Lane, Sebastopol, CA 95472.